Page 4

TALES OF THE SLAYER
The Broken Bottle of Djinn

Based on the television series created by JOSS WHEDON
Story JANE ESPENSON and DOUGLAS PETRIE
Art JEFF MATSUDA and GENE COLAN
Colours DAVE STEWART
Letters PAT BROSSEAU for BLAMBOT
US Editor SCOTT ALLIE

Page 14

WILLOW & TARA
Wilderness (Part 1)

Based on the television series created by JOSS WHEDON
Story AMBER BENSON and CHRISTOPHER GOLDEN
Pencils AJ Inks DEREK FRIDOLFS
Colours MICHELLE MADSEN
Letters MICHAEL HEISLER
US Editor SCOTT ALLIE

Page 39

WILLOW & TARA
Wilderness (Part 2)

Based on the television series created by JOSS WHEDON
Story AMBER BENSON and CHRISTOPHER GOLDEN
Pencils AJ and KLEBS
Inks DEREK FRIDOLFS and FABIO LAGUNA
Colours MICHELLE MADSEN Letters MICHAEL HEISLER
US Editor SCOTT ALLIE

**Published by Pedigree Books Limited
Beech Hill House, Walmnut Gardens,
St. David's Hill, Exeter, EX4 4DH
E-mail books@pedigreegroup.co.uk
Published 2003**

£6.99

TALES OF THE SLAYER
The Broken Bottle of Djinn

Willow & Tara

Buffy the Vampire Slayer

WILLOW & TARA

Wilderness (Part 1)

TARA, BABY, CAN YOU HAND ME ANOTHER ONE OF THOSE TUMMY-YUMMY SEAWEED ROLLS?

THAT'S DISGUSTING, YOU GUYS. *SEAWEED* ROLLS? YUCK!

I GOT *YOU* SOME POTATO CHIPS, SO NO NEED TO WORRY ABOUT UCKY SEAWEEDNESS.

ARE YOU HAVING A GOOD TIME, DAWNIE? I FEEL BAD, US DRAGGING YOU AROUND TO ALL THOSE WITCHY PLACES--

YOU GUYS, I'M HAVING FUN.

I COULD HAVE OPTED FOR DISNEYLAND WITH XANDER AND ANYA, BUT TRUST ME, CHECKING OUT MAGICAL POWER SPOTS AND HAUNTED BEACHES WITH YOU GUYS IS, LIKE, WAY MORE EXCITING.

YOU MEAN TWO GRAFFITI-COVERED INDIAN ROCK CIRCLES AND A NON-HAUNTED, HAUNTED BEACH? THAT WAS EXCITING?

COME ON, YOU TWO! GHOSTIES ASIDE, THIS IS GONNA BE A GIRL-POWER EXTRAVAGANZA. JUST LEAVING THE SUNNYDALE ZIP CODE WITH MY TWO FAVORITE WOMEN MAKES FOR HAPPY WILLOWNESS.

FINDING SOME POWER SPOTS WITH *ACTUAL* MAGIC IS ONLY ICING ON THE CAKE THAT IS VACATION.

YUM! THIS IS SCRUMMYLICIOUS! WHO NEEDS NASTY OL' MEAT ANYWAY.

WHAT I ALWAYS SAY.

WHAT DO YOU THINK'S GOING ON OVER THERE, WILLOW?

MATSUDA PL.

ONE WAY →

GET LOST!

NO COMPROMISE

LEAVE OUR TREES

GO HOME

LEAVE LOGG

"WITHOUT A CLUE. BUT NOT MUCH OF THE 'GOOD WILL TOWARD YOUR FELLOW MAN,' HUH?"

IN MY SCIENCE CLASS, WE HAD, LIKE, THIS BIG GROUP DISCUSSION ABOUT HOW HORRIBLE DEFORESTATION AND STUFF IS. IT'S LIKE BURNING DOWN YOUR OWN HOUSE!

THE KID'S GOT THE RIGHT IDEA. THEM LOGGERS THINK JUST 'CAUSE THE GOVERNMENT OWNS THE LAND AND PAYS THEM WELL TO DO IT, THAT IT'S OKAY TO RIP APART OUR WOODS.

BUT WHAT GOES AROUND, COMES AROUND. BELIEVE YOU ME LADIES, THIS I KNOW.

JEEZ, THAT GUY WAS DEFINITELY "GULP" WORTHY.

A T-TRIPLE "GULP," IN MY BOOK.

CAN WE COUNT ON YOU GIRLS TO SIGN OUR PETITION?

I GUESS THAT DEPENDS ON WHAT YOU'RE PETITIONING FOR.

WE'RE NOT... LOCAL. WHAT'S GOING ON?

"THIS IS VIRGIN REDWOOD UP HERE. FIRST GROWTH TREES. PROBABLY THOUSANDS OF YEARS OLD..."

...YOU DESTROY THOSE OLD FELLOWS AND OUR EARTH GOES WITH THEM!

HOW CAN ANYONE JUST CUT THEM DOWN? TREES ARE LIVING THINGS, TOO! MIGHT AS WELL JUST CUT A BUNCH OF PEOPLE DOWN!

IT'S ALL RIGHT, DAWNIE.

IT'S **NOT** ALL RIGHT! NOTHING IS ALL RIGHT!

EXCUSE ME, YOU'RE--

IT'S THE FOREST FIGHTING BACK!

THE TREES AND ANIMALS ARE UNDER THE SPELL OF GAEA! AND SHE SEEKS TO DESTROY US ALL!! THEY SAY THE ANIMALS DIDN'T KILL THEM, BUT--

BEWARE THE WOODS! THE EARTH MOTHER WILL KILL YOU, IF YOU TRESPASS ON HER LAND!

DOLORES! SHHHH!

HER HUSBAND WAS A LOGGER. HE WAS KILLED UP IN THE WOODS EARLIER THIS YEAR. THEY SAY IT WAS AN ACCIDENT, BUT DOLORES SWEARS A PACK OF SQUIRRELS ATTACKED HIM. IT'S INSANITY!

KILLER SQUIRRELS? YOU HAVE GOT TO BE KIDDING ME!

THAT WAS AWFUL. THE POOR WOMAN--

I KNOW-- IT'S NOT FUNNY. BUT...THE SQUIRRELS...

HA HA HA HA HA

YOU'RE BOTH RIGHT. CUTE YET HOMICIDAL FOREST CREATURES AREN'T THE KIND OF THING YOU EXPECT FROM A BENEVOLENT EARTH GODDESS.

CLICK

THERE'S SOMETHING NOT QUITE RIGHT ABOUT THIS PLACE. IF GILES WERE HERE, HE'D BE HAVING A GLASSES-CLEANING MARATHON.

LET'S CHECK OUT THE ALTAR OF THE GREEN. IF THERE'S ANY MALEVOLENT SUPERNATURAL DOINGS AROUND HERE, WE'LL SENSE IT THERE.

CALIFORNIA 1RWL494

VRRMM

IT'S PROBABLY JUST A BUNCH OF WHOOEY TO KEEP PEOPLE OUT OF THE FOREST, ANYWAY.

TRYING TO SAVE THE FOREST BY TELLING TALL TALES? I DON'T KNOW, TARA.

OR, HEY, GUYS, MAYBE THE LOGGER WAS KILLED BY LITTLE FURRY DEMONS AND HIS WIFE JUST ASSUMED RABID SQUIRRELS. LITTLE, SQUIRREL-SHAPED DEMONS.

AND NOW I'M CREEPING MYSELF OUT!

22

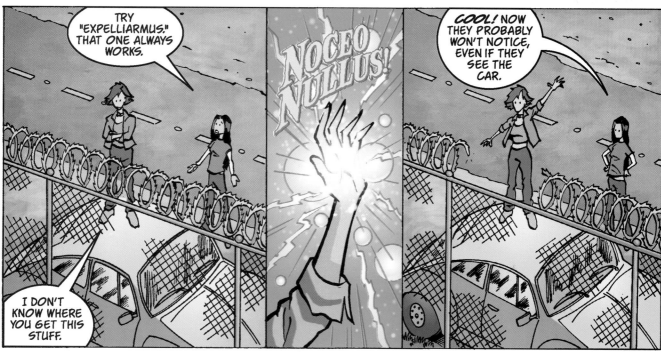

UH... WILLOW?

NO DANCING NAKED, HUH? SIGH. IT JUST WON'T BE THE SAME.

THAT'S ALL RIGHT, WE CAN SAVE IT FOR LATER.

LIONS AND TIGERS AND--

HAH! SEE? THE HIGH-SCHOOL KID ISN'T THE ONLY ONE GETTING WEIRD VIBES. DO YOU THINK THE WOODS ARE HAUNTED?

YOU GUYS, DO SOMETHING!

WILLOW, CAN YOU FEEL IT? DARKNESS. IT'S C-COMING OFF THE BUCK IN WAVES.

THERE'S SOMETHING ELSE RUNNING THE SHOW HERE. LET'S GET RID OF IT.

PULSES DISCEDO!

IS HE--?

YEAH. GUESS THE SQUIRREL WOMAN BACK IN TOWN WASN'T SO CRAZY AFTER ALL.

COME ON, DAWN. YOU'RE GOING TO THE HOTEL. THEN TARA AND I WILL COME BACK AND TRACK DOWN WHATEVER'S DOING ALL THIS.

I'M NOT GOING ANYWHERE. WE'VE GOT TO STOP THIS BEFORE SOMEONE ELSE DIES.

WHATEVER M-MALEVOLENCE IS INFLUENCING THIS, IT'S NOT EVEN TRYING TO COVER ITS TRACKS. IT'S COMING FROM THE SAME DIRECTION AS THE ALTAR OF THE GREEN.

STICK RIGHT WITH US.

HEY, I'M GLUE. VERY STICKY.

WILLOW, DO YOU THINK WE C-CAN--

START BACKING UP, SLOWLY.

KEEP YOUR EYES OPEN, DAWN. I DON'T THINK IT'S OVER YET.

WE DROVE THE ANIMALS AWAY. IF YOU WANT TO KILL US--WHATEVER YOU ARE--YOU'RE GOING TO HAVE TO COME OUT AND DO IT YOURSELF.

UM, WILLOW... IS THAT REALLY A GOOD IDEA?

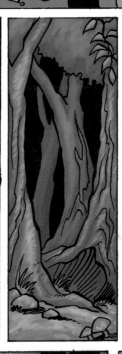

skritch

witches should be 'shamed of themselves, they should. humans destroy the green.

we tries to stop it. witches should be helping us...

...not them.

GET IT OFF!! GODDESS, GET IT OFF ME!!

I CAN'T...IT'S LIKE MAGIC DOESN'T AFFECT IT...

WE DIDN'T COME HERE TO HARM YOU, BUT GET IT OFF HER *NOW* OR IN HECATE'S NAME *I WILL KILL YOU ALL!*

draw back the boggart.

IT'S...IT'S DISGUSTING. WHEN IT TOUCHES YOU ...IT FEELS SO FILTHY.

we of the woodkin did not put bloodlust in the animals. woodkin do not kill. mayhap you see the altar, talk to the king, witches help us after all.

MAYHAP.

HUMAN BEINGS CAN BE PRETTY MUCH THOUGHTLESS A LOT OF TIMES...

AND THEY CAN BE KINDA GREEDY-LIKE SOMETIMES... MAJORLY SELF-INVOLVED AND...

WOW. NOT SO PRETTY PICTURE ON THE WHOLE HUMAN RACE, HUH?

WILLOW'S NOT DOING SO WELL ON EXPLAINING THE WHOLE "HUMAN BEINGS ARE REALLY NICE DEEP DOWN" THING.

SHE'S...JUST TRYING TO PRESENT A FAIR PICTURE.

I THINK.

methinks i understand you, witch -- human beings are silly and not understanding what they do somes of the times.

YOU GOT THAT FROM WHAT I SAID?

SMART SPRITE.

we not hate humans, witch. sad as we are to do the not nice, we are bound. we understands you, witch, but Jack would disembowel us all if we not bow to his orders.

WHO'S JACK?

Jack! come out and play! we brings witches what says they wants to help.

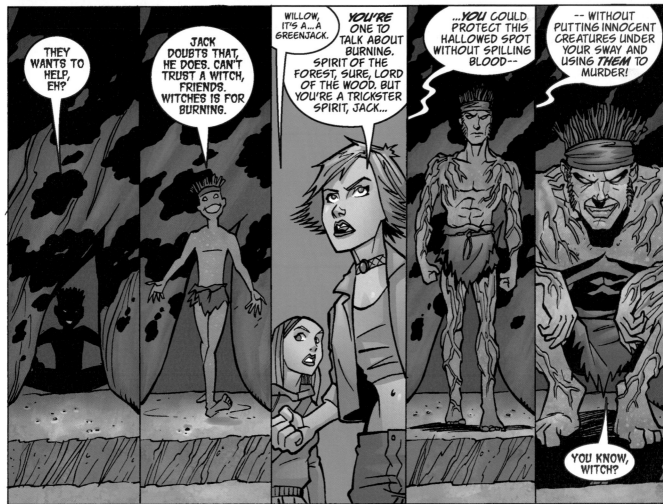

THEY WANTS TO HELP, EH?

JACK DOUBTS THAT, HE DOES. CAN'T TRUST A WITCH, FRIENDS. WITCHES IS FOR BURNING.

WILLOW, IT'S A...A GREENJACK. YOU'RE ONE TO TALK ABOUT BURNING. SPIRIT OF THE FOREST, SURE, LORD OF THE WOOD. BUT YOU'RE A TRICKSTER SPIRIT, JACK...

...YOU COULD PROTECT THIS HALLOWED SPOT WITHOUT SPILLING BLOOD--

-- WITHOUT PUTTING INNOCENT CREATURES UNDER YOUR SWAY AND USING THEM TO MURDER!

YOU KNOW, WITCH?

Buffy the Vampire Slayer

Pinup 4

WILLOW & TARA
Wilderness (Part 2)

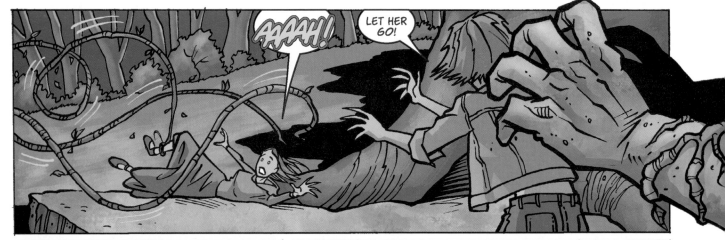

STOP IT! PLEASE!!

THIS ISN'T WHAT YOU'RE SUPPOSED TO BE! ALL THE CUTTING -- IT'S TWISTED YOU AROUND -- MADE YOU CRAZY. GRIEF *DOES* THAT.

DAWN! GET BACK!

Y-YOU'RE THE KING OF THE WOOD...PURE AND... AND NOBLE AND...

OH, JACK IS *KING*, GIRL.

NOW THE KING CALLS THE WOOD *TO WAR!!*

STRIP HER FLESH FROM HER BONES!

no Jack!

bad Jack!

harm not this girl!

she cries for us!

FOOLISH SPRITES!

THE GIRL'S PREYED ON YOUR *WEAK NATURE.* IF YOU WILL NOT HELP ME SAVE THE ALTAR, I WILL DO IT *ALONE!*

I WILL PAINT EVERY TREE WITH HUMAN BLOOD!

THANKS, YOU GUYS.

HE'S...HE'S GONE.

AND THIS IS ME NOW HAVING A REALLY BAD FEELING THAT I KNOW WHERE HE WENT.

THAT WAS PRETTY BRAVE, DAWNIE.

I CAN BE BRAVE. I'VE HAD THE BEST TEACHERS.

THANKS. BUT JUST, OKAY, MAYBE *NOT* TELLING BUFFY ABOUT THIS PART OF THE TRIP.

NO KIDDING. LIKE SHE'D EVER LET ME GO ANYWHERE WITH YOU GUYS AGAIN. *"THOSE WITCHES, THEY'RE TROUBLE MAGNETS!"*

SERIOUSLY, WILLOW, I THOUGHT HE'D HURT YOU BAD.

NOPE. STILL FULLY FUNCTIONING WILLOW. OR MAYBE 90 PERCENT. THANKS TO YOU TWO, AND THANKS TO THE LIKING THE LITTLE FOLKS HAVE TAKEN TO DAWN.

IF YOU'RE O-OKAY, WILL, WE SHOULD GO.

I DON'T GET IT. IT'S SUNRISE, BUT WE WEREN'T IN THERE ANYWHERE NEAR --

YOU NEVER READ FAERIE TALES? MORTALS WANDER INTO A FAERIE WOOD, TIME GETS ALL WONKY. IT'S TRADITIONAL.

OH. WEIRD. ANY THOUGHTS ON WHAT WE *DO* NOW?

YOU *DID* HEAR THAT PART ABOUT PAINTING EVERY TREE WITH HUMAN BLOOD? NOT GIVING US MUCH CHOICE. WE FIND GREENJACK...

...AND WE BURN HIM DOWN.

WILLOW, WE CAN'T. MYSTICAL CREATURES DON'T EXIST UNDER THE SAME RULES AS WE DO. IN THEIR EYES, THEY'RE JUST FIGHTING BACK.

HOW ARE WE ANY BETTER IF WE JUST KILL GREENJACK?

A GREENJACK'S ONLY *PART* OF A GREATER FORCE. IF WE DESTROY HIM, HE'LL JUST GO SOMEPLACE ELSE. 'COURSE, THEN HE'LL BE P.O.'ED, SO OKAY, WE *COULD* TRY TO TRAP HIM, TRY TO MAKE HIM SEE REASON.

I'VE GOT SOME SPELLS IN MIND TO HOLD HIM TEMPORARILY, UNTIL WE MAKE HIM REALIZE WE WANT TO HELP.

OKAY...

"...LET'S JUST HOPE 'TEMPORARILY' IS LONG ENOUGH."

LORD, I'M BEAT. WHEN THIS JOB IS FINISHED, I'M GONNA SLEEP FOR ABOUT A YEAR.

GARY! HEY, GARY!

YOU THINK MAYBE YOU COULD GET SOME COFFEE IN HERE THAT DOESN'T TASTE LIKE SLUDGE?

COFFEE'S THE LEAST OF OUR TROUBLES.

WE HAD ANOTHER DEATH. ONE OF THE RANGERS, LAST NIGHT. TRAMPLED TO DEATH.

JESUS.

SOMEONE'S REALLY GOT IT IN FOR US. THEY DON'T PAY US ENOUGH FOR THIS.

THEY SAY IT'S ANIMALS, FREAK ATTACKS AND STUFF. AND YEAH, I'VE SEEN THOSE VIDEO SHOWS ON TV, "WHEN ANIMALS ATTACK."

BUT THIS IS TOO MUCH. MAKES YOU WONDER IF SOMEBODY ELSE IS BEHIND IT. SOME OF THE TREE HUGGERS SURE HATE US ENOUGH TO DO SOMETHING SICK.

WORST PART IS, I LOOK AROUND AND I UNDERSTAND WHY.

WHAT ARE YOU *TALKING* ABOUT, MAN?

PEOPLE HAVE BEEN CUTTING DOWN TREES SINCE MAN WALKED UPRIGHT. TO BUILD HOUSES AND CARVE CANOES AND MAKE FIRES. THIS IS NO DIFFERENT.

MAYBE IT *IS* DIFFERENT. WE DON'T CREATE ANYTHING, DON'T GROW ANYTHING, JUST DESTROY. I GUESS I'M NOT CUT OUT TO HAVE A JOB WHERE PEOPLE HATE ME. IF I COULD AFFORD TO QUIT, I WOULD.

MAYBE YOU'LL GET LUCKY. MAYBE THE PROTESTORS'LL SHUT US DOWN. BUT THERE AREN'T ANY EASY ANSWERS, MAN. SO WE JUST DO THE WORK, COLLECT OUR PAY.

RIGHT, WE GO BACK TO WORK. I GUESS I JUST WISH WE WEREN'T SO GOOD AT IT.

AAAEEGHHHH!

WHAT THE--

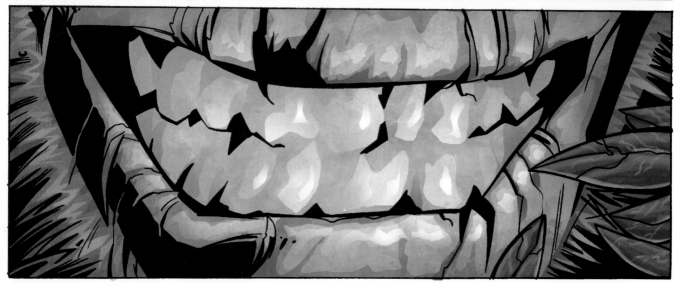

YOU HAVE TO STOP, JACK. IT SHOULDN'T HAVE TO BE LIKE THIS.

WE ADMIT IT, OKAY? HUMANS ARE STUPID AND VICIOUS. WE WANT TO HELP. WE *CAN* HELP. JUST DON'T MAKE US HAVE TO CHOOSE BETWEEN HELPING YOU AND SAVING HUMAN LIVES.

HUMAN LIVES? WHAT OF THE *THOUSANDS* OF LIVES HUMANS HAVE TAKEN HERE IN THE WOOD? LOOK AROUND, *WITCHES!*

THEY MUST DIE.

HE'S NOT LISTENING, TARA. WE CAN'T LET HIM KILL ANYBODY ELSE. SPECIFICALLY, AT THE MOMENT, *US!*

THEY KILL THE WOOD, DESTROY THE SACRED PLACES! FOR EVERY TREE FELLED, I CUT DOWN A HUMAN!

AND I START WITH *TRAITOROUS WITCHES!*

NOW.

GRRRRR

ICE!

WE DID IT.

SO WE DID. WOULDJA LOOK AT THAT? WE'RE LIKE THE WONDER TWINS. IF THEY WERE WITCHES... AND IN LOVE...

...BUT, Y'KNOW, NOT SIBLINGS.

DIE WITCHES!!! YOU HAVE DEFILED THE HEART OF THE WOOD!

THAT'S ENOUGH!!!

BAM

LET'S GIVE IT THE OLD SUNNYDALE TRY.

WHOA! I STILL DON'T GET THE WHOLE WEIRDO HOUSE STUFF, WILL--

I'VE GOT IT!

I FIGURED OUT HOW THIS SPELL WAS CAST! NOW WE JUST HAVE TO REPLICATE IT!

IT WON'T BE EASY, BUT STRONG MAGIC NEVER IS...

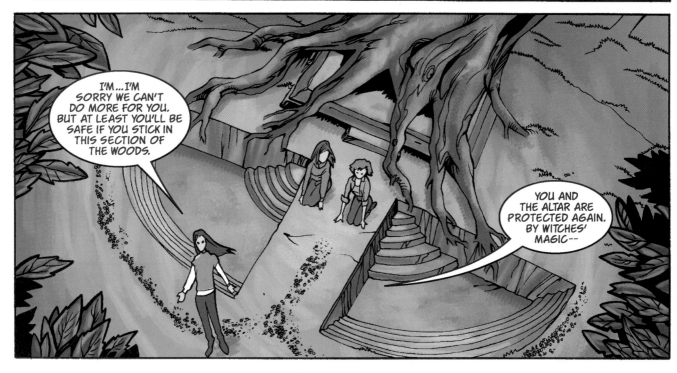

I'M...I'M SORRY WE CAN'T DO MORE FOR YOU. BUT AT LEAST YOU'LL BE SAFE IF YOU STICK IN THIS SECTION OF THE WOODS.

YOU AND THE ALTAR ARE PROTECTED AGAIN, BY WITCHES' MAGIC--

REAL PEOPLE-- Y'KNOW, HUMANS-- WON'T BE ABLE TO SEE YOU ANYMORE.

NO HIKERS-- NO LOGGERS. NO ONE WHO MIGHT HURT YOU.

ONLY THE KING OF THE WOOD CAN INVITE HUMANS BACK INTO THIS PART OF THE WOOD.

MAYBE HE WILL SOMEDAY. WHEN PEOPLE LEARN TO LIVE WITH NATURE INSTEAD OF DESTROYING IT.

THAT WAS BEAUTIFUL, DAWNIE.

LOOK!

...king of the wood will come again, he will...

HEY SWEETIE, HOW LONG BEFORE THE GREENJACK REMANIFESTS, DO YA THINK?

I DON'T KNOW. I JUST HOPE IT'S A MORE GREENJACK-FRIENDLY PLACE WHEN HE DOES DECIDE TO COME BACK.

THE END